Catholic
Funny Fill-Ins

Saints Spectacular!

CATHOLIC
Funny
FILL-INS

Saints Spectacular!

Written by Karen and Tommy Tighe

Illustrated by Jason Bach

Pauline
BOOKS & MEDIA
Boston

Nihil Obstat:
Reverend Thomas W. Buckley, S.T.D., S.S.L.

Imprimatur:
✠ Seán Cardinal O'Malley, O.F.M. Cap.
Archbishop of Boston
October 2, 2019

ISBN 10: 0–8198-1674-4
ISBN 13: 978–0-8198-1674-0

Cover and interior design by Mary Joseph Peterson, FSP
Cover and interior illustrations by Jason Bach

Published by Pauline Books & Media, 50 Saint Pauls Avenue, Boston, MA 02130–3491

Printed in the U.S.A.

CFFSS VSAUSAPEOILL12-1210158 1674-4

www.pauline.org

Pauline Books & Media is the publishing house of the Daughters of St. Paul, an international congregation of women religious serving the Church with the communications media.

1 2 3 4 5 6 7 8 9   24 23 22 21 20

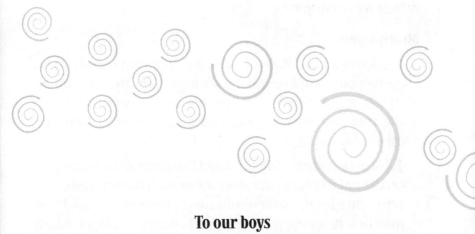

To our boys

James, Paul, Andrew, Luke, and Charlie.

You are the joy of our lives!

How to Play

Catholic Funny Fill-Ins is easy, fun, and can be played by one or more people.

Multiplayer

1. *Choose a story*. Will you have a picnic with friends? Help name your brand new baby sibling? Want to brush up on trivia about the saints? You decide. Just remember to keep the title and topic of your chosen story secret from the other players!

2. *Fill in the word list*. Read aloud the parts of speech listed on the page before your story. After each part of speech (or other category), pause until a player gives you a word that matches it (*example*: if you read "noun," a player might respond with "table"). Use a pencil to write the words you hear on the blanks.

3. *Read, laugh, and repeat*. Once you have filled in all the blanks, read the story aloud using the words your players came up with. Get ready for stories that might be funny, strange, or wacky—but always unique and always something you created! End your story by sharing the "Did You Know?" at the bottom of the page. Then, pass the book to the next player for another round of *Catholic Funny Fill-Ins* fun.

Single Player

By yourself? Follow the same instructions above—just be extra careful to cover the story when you fill out the word list.

Did You Know ... ?

Catholic Funny Fill-Ins are meant to be silly while also teaching you something about our Catholic faith. Don't miss the "Did You Know?" section at the end of each story. It has saintly profiles, fascinating trivia, and creative ways to help you grow in your faith and in your relationship with Christ and his Church.

Parts of Speech

To create your *Catholic Funny Fill-Ins* stories, you need to know the parts of speech. Here is a short list you can refer to while playing:

NOUN: a person, place, or thing (examples: cat, sandwich, trampoline, Vatican City, nun)

PLURAL NOUN: more than one person, place, or thing (examples: cats, sandwiches, cities, saints)

ADJECTIVE: a word that describes a noun (examples: smart, stinky, gooey, delicious, fast)

VERB: an action or state of being (examples: run, jump, swing, eat, chew, cry, swim, twirl)

VERB PAST TENSE: an action that happened in the past (examples: ran, jumped, swung, ate, chewed, cried, swam, twirled)

VERB ENDING IN "ING": an ongoing action (examples: running, jumping, sewing, crying)

ADVERB: a word that describes a verb and answers the questions *When?* or *How?* Adverbs often end in "ly" (examples: quickly, happily, slowly)

EXCLAMATION: something you might suddenly call out (examples: ah-ha, ouch, wow, yikes)

When a blank asks for something that is not a part of speech (examples: number, animal, food, or body part), use any word that fits in that category (examples: one million, dog, pizza, or ear lobe).

NAME OF FEMALE IN THE ROOM _____

ADJECTIVE _____

COLOR _____

ADJECTIVE _____

ADJECTIVE _____

PLURAL FOOD _____

ADJECTIVE _____

ROOM IN HOUSE _____

ADJECTIVE _____

ADJECTIVE _____

PLURAL FOOD _____

PLURAL VEGETABLE _____

VERB _____

FAVORITE FOOD _____

PLURAL TYPE OF FLOWER _____

The Legend of Saint Brigid

It was the last day of January, and my Grandma _____
NAME OF FEMALE IN ROOM

was visiting from Ireland! Having her around was _____ and
ADJECTIVE

my sister and I just loved all the things she'd tell us about life on the

_____ Isle!
COLOR

Grandma told us about Saint Brigid and her _____ cow.
ADJECTIVE

Saint Brigid is the _____ patron saint of Ireland and a very
ADJECTIVE

holy woman. One time, Brigid gave all of her family's _____
PLURAL FOOD

to the poor. When her family found out, they were _____
ADJECTIVE

with anger, but Brigid said a prayer and their _____ was
ROOM IN HOUSE

miraculously full of _____ food once again!
ADJECTIVE

Grandma said Saint Brigid's feast day has some _____
ADJECTIVE

traditions. First, if you leave out _____ for her and
PLURAL FOOD

_____ for her cow, the legend is that she will
PLURAL VEGETABLE

_____ by and bless your garden! With her blessing, I wonder
VERB

if we'll get _____ to grow in our garden this year!
FAVORITE FOOD

Did you know . . . ?

Saint Brigid is one of the most well-known Irish saints. There are many legends about
her life. According to one legend, Saint Brigid helped a dying man to become Christian
after she wove him a cross out of rushes. You can make your own Saint Brigid's Cross out
of reeds, straw, or even pipe cleaners to hang up in your house. Who knows, Saint Brigid
may even come by with her cow and bless your _____ !
PLURAL TYPE OF FLOWER

NAME OF PERSON IN ROOM _____

SPORT _____

SPORT _____

NOUN _____

ADJECTIVE _____

NUMBER _____

VERB ENDING IN "ING" _____

TYPE OF CONTAINER _____

ADJECTIVE ENDING IN "EST" _____

VERB ENDING IN "ING" _____

PLURAL NOUN _____

EXCLAMATION _____

LIQUID _____

PLURAL BODY PART _____

VERB _____

ADVERB _____

I Love Sports

I love to play sports! My best friend _____ is incredible

NAME OF PERSON IN ROOM

at _____ , and my cousin loves to play _____ , but,

SPORT   SPORT

my favorite sport is a game I made up myself. It's called _____

NOUN

ball. It's my favorite thing to do on a/an _____ summer day.

ADJECTIVE

To play, you need at least _____ people on each team. The

NUMBER

game starts with one team _____ around the field. The

VERB ENDING IN "ING"

second team tries to get the ball past them and into the

_____ at the far end of the field. The _____

TYPE OF CONTAINER   ADJECTIVE ENDING IN "EST"

part is getting past the other team without _____ . The team

VERB ENDING IN "ING"

with the most _____ at the end, wins!

PLURAL NOUN

At the end of a long game, it's always a good idea to show good

sportsmanship by saying " _____ " to the other team no matter

EXCLAMATION

who won. Also, to reduce soreness, be sure to drink some

_____ and stretch all of the muscles in your _____ .

LIQUID   PLURAL BODY PART

Nothing beats having fun playing sports with friends!

Did you know . . . ?

Blessed Pier Giorgio Frassati (1901–1925) was a young Italian athlete. He loved all different kinds of sports, especially mountain climbing. He shared the Gospel with fellow competitors and adventure seekers. He once wrote *verso l'alto* which means "to the heights," on the back of a photo of himself mountain climbing. This has become the motto of many people who have a devotion to Blessed Pier Giorgio. If you had a personal motto, would it be

" _____ _____ "?

VERB   ADVERB

MONTH _____

NAME OF RELATIVE _____

PLURAL NOUN _____

PLURAL NOUN _____

ADJECTIVE _____

LARGE NUMBER _____

ADVERB _____

ADJECTIVE _____

NAME OF PERSON IN ROOM _____

VERY LONG NAME _____

FAMOUS PERSON _____

SAINT'S NAME _____

FIRST PERSON WHO COMES TO YOUR MIND

_____

NAME OF A FRIEND _____

ADJECTIVE _____

VERB _____

What's In a Name?

Our family is having a new baby this ________________ ! We are all
MONTH

so excited, especially ______________ ! Mom and Dad have asked for
NAME OF RELATIVE

help to get ready, so I've been doing all kinds of things like washing the

baby ______________ , shopping for ______________ , and building the
PLURAL NOUN PLURAL NOUN

______________ crib.
ADJECTIVE

After doing chores for what seemed like ______________ days, I
LARGE NUMBER

______________ complained to Mom and asked for something more
ADVERB

exciting to help with. She said I could help pick out a/an

______________ name for the baby. That sounded like a great idea!
ADJECTIVE

I made a list of names I liked: I wrote down ________________ ,
NAME OF PERSON IN ROOM

________________ , and my personal favorite, ______________ . When
VERY LONG NAME FAMOUS PERSON

the time came, we took turns suggesting the names we liked. Then Dad had an idea: he looked at the calendar to see what feast days were close to the baby's due date. That's how they picked my name! We found some

great names like ______________ and Saint ________________ . All
SAINT'S NAME FIRST PERSON WHO COMES TO MIND

of these saints led heroic lives and would be a great patron saint to have.

In the end, we decided to pick ______________ . We think it's absolutely
NAME OF FRIEND

______________ !
ADJECTIVE

Did you know . . . ?

Oftentimes, parents will name their children after a saint. If this is true for you, a great thing to do is to learn about the saint with whom you share a name. Not named after a saint? Try finding out about the saint whose feast day is your birthday. Born on the extra day in a leap year? There's a saint for that too! Oh, by the way, you don't have to ______________ the way your patron saint(s) did.
VERB

ADJECTIVE _____

ADJECTIVE _____

BODY PART _____

ITEM FOUND IN BATHROOM _____

ADVERB _____

ADJECTIVE _____

ARTICLE OF CLOTHING _____

ANIMAL _____

PLURAL ANIMAL _____

NUMBER _____

ADJECTIVE _____

FAMOUS PERSON _____

ADVERB _____

ADJECTIVE _____

NAME OF PERSON IN ROOM _____

My First Communion

I heard that you are nervous about your first Communion, so let me

give you some _____ advice. First I'll tell you about the day I
ADJECTIVE

received my first Communion. I woke up with a/an _____ smile
ADJECTIVE

on my _____ , but then so many things seemed to go wrong.
BODY PART

The _____ was broken, so I couldn't take a shower. No
ITEM FOUND IN BATHROOM

big deal, I just _____ got dressed in my _____
ADVERB   ADJECTIVE

_____ and started to look for my shoes. But then I found our
ARTICLE OF CLOTHING

pet _____ chewing on them! I had to wear them anyway.
ANIMAL

I thought it couldn't get worse, but then a group of _____
PLURAL ANIMAL

were crossing the street and blocking the way. We had to wait

_____ minutes and I became really impatient and I felt
NUMBER

_____ .
ADJECTIVE

Then I remembered _____ telling me about Blessed Imelda
FAMOUS PERSON

Lambertini, the patron of first communicants. I _____ said a
ADVERB

prayer for her intercession. Although the day was _____ , it
ADJECTIVE

sure was very memorable. So whatever happens on your big day,

remember to ask for Blessed Imelda Lambertini to help you out just like

she helped me.

Did you know . . . ?

Blessed Imelda Lambertini (1322–1333) was an Italian girl who wished to receive her first Communion on her fifth birthday. At that time, the Church required children to be at least twelve years old before receiving Communion. But Blessed Imelda loved Jesus with all her heart and wanted to be united with him in the Eucharist. One day while Blessed Imelda was praying before the tabernacle, a miracle happened: the tabernacle door opened and the Host floated toward her! When the priest saw this, he knew God wanted him to give Blessed Imelda Communion right then and there. Has _____ received first
NAME OF PERSON IN ROOM
Communion yet? What does he/she remember about this special day?

ADJECTIVE _____

CITY _____

NUMBER _____

BODY PART _____

COLOR _____

FOOD _____

ADJECTIVE _____

FOOD _____

LARGE NUMBER _____

ADJECTIVE _____

TYPE OF CONTAINER _____

ADJECTIVE _____

ANIMAL _____

PLURAL NOUN _____

Miracle Meal

Last week, I had the most _____ meal. My parents and I

ADJECTIVE

went to _____ to hear a man named Jesus preach. His

CITY OR TOWN

preaching lasted over _____ hour(s) and I could feel my

NUMBER

_____ start to rumble.

BODY PART

Thankfully, a man with a long _____ beard told everyone

COLOR

to sit down in groups so they could feed us. What a relief! I hoped they

would give us _____ and _____ _____

FOOD ADJECTIVE FOOD

to eat. Jesus said a blessing over a small plate. I looked around and

noticed that there were about _____ people there. I was

LARGE NUMBER

_____ with worry that there wouldn't be enough food to eat.

ADJECTIVE

When a/an _____ came around with some fish and bread

TYPE OF CONTAINER

in it, I took just enough food to make sure there would be enough for

everyone. Yum! It was a/an _____ meal. After we had

ADJECTIVE

finished, someone came around to collect any food that was left over.

To my surprise, I looked down and noticed there was still enough food

on my plate to feed a hungry _____ . I was so stuffed, I

ANIMAL

couldn't believe it! How did I eat so much but still have so much left on

my plate?

Did you know . . . ?

You can read about the miraculous Feeding of the Five Thousand in all four Gospels. The Gospels of Matthew, Mark, Luke, and John were written by four different saints who wanted the whole world to know about Jesus' life and ministry. Saint Matthew was a tax collector whom Jesus named one of his twelve apostles. Saint Mark worked closely with Saint Peter during the early years of the Church. Saint Luke was a doctor and friend of Saint Paul. Saint John was the youngest of the twelve apostles. Imagine if Jesus had multiplied

_____ . That would make for a very different event!

PLURAL NOUN

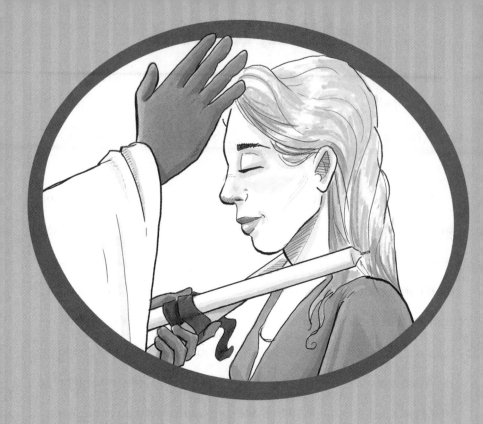

ADJECTIVE _____

SMALL NUMBER _____

ADJECTIVE _____

ANIMAL _____

NOUN _____

BODY PART _____

NOUN _____

EXCLAMATION _____

ADJECTIVE _____

PROFESSION _____

LIQUID _____

PIECE OF FURNITURE _____

NUMBER _____

VERB PAST TENSE _____

NAME OF MALE IN ROOM _____

PLURAL BODY PART _____

PLURAL FOOD _____

NOUN _____

Blessing of Throats

My _____ sister woke up at _____ in the
     ADJECTIVE   SMALL NUMBER

morning feeling _____ . She felt like she had a/an
                  ADJECTIVE

_____ in her throat!
  ANIMAL

"Dad, help! My throat feels like a/an _____ ," she said.
                                NOUN

Dad rushed in and checked her _____ for a fever. "Open
                         BODY PART

wide," he said, and he used a/an _____ to look in her mouth.
                        NOUN

" _____ ! I've never seen a throat so _____ before.
  EXCLAMATION   ADJECTIVE

We'd better take you to see the _____ ."
                      PROFESSION

After being examined, it turned out she had an infection and was

told to drink warm _____ and relax on the _____
              LIQUID   FURNITURE

in the living room for the next _____ days.
                    NUMBER

As we _____ home, we realized that today was the feast
     VERB PAST TENSE

of Saint Blaise, the patron saint of people who suffer from illnesses of

the throat! We pulled over at the church to get a blessing from Father

_____ . He blessed everyone's throats and _____ .
NAME OF MALE IN ROOM   PLURAL BODY PART

After that, we all felt better, knowing that God was in control, so Dad

treated us to frosty _____ .
              PLURAL FOOD

Did you know ... ?

Does your parish offer a blessing of throats on the feast of Saint Blaise (February 3)? Saint Blaise was a third-century doctor who became a Catholic bishop. He is known as the patron saint of throats and throat illnesses because he once saved a young boy from choking on a _____ . On his feast day, many priests will invite people to come
        NOUN
forward during Mass for a special blessing of the throat. The priest holds two blessed, unlit candles next to each person's throat and asks Saint Blaise to pray for them.

NAME OF FEMALE IN ROOM _____

ADJECTIVE _____

PLURAL NOUN _____

ADJECTIVE _____

ADJECTIVE _____

VERB _____

VERB _____

ADJECTIVE _____

BODY PART _____

ADJECTIVE _____

ADJECTIVE ENDING IN "EST" _____

VERB ENDING IN "ING" _____

ADJECTIVE _____

PLURAL NOUN _____

Twin Sister

People always ask my twin sister _____ and me what

NAME OF FEMALE IN ROOM

it's like to be twins. Well, for starters, having a twin is like getting a best

friend at birth. We have a/an _____ bond that can't be

ADJECTIVE

denied. After all, we share our room, our _____ , and have the

PLURAL NOUN

same birthday! When you're a twin, people always ask you who was

born _____ . They want to know the differences between us,

ADJECTIVE

like who is more _____ and if we both like to

ADJECTIVE

_____ and _____ . Sometimes it's hard for people

VERB ____ VERB

to tell us apart, but one easy way is that I have _____ hair

ADJECTIVE

and she has a smaller _____ . Since we're always being

BODY PART

compared, you'd think we would get _____ about it, but

ADJECTIVE

we're used to it. Probably the _____ thing about being a

ADJECTIVE ENDING IN "EST"

twin is being able to know what the other twin is _____ at all

VERB ENDING IN "ING"

times. I love my twin! She is so _____ —just like me!

ADJECTIVE

Did you know . . . ?

Saint Benedict (c. 480–547) and Saint Scholastica (c. 480–543) were twins who had a really special relationship. Saint Benedict used to visit Saint Scholastica at her convent, where they would enjoy deep, faith-filled conversations. One time when they were together, Saint Scholastica asked Saint Benedict to spend the night, but he declined. So Saint Scholastica asked God to make Saint Benedict stay. Not long after, a storm broke out and Saint Benedict could not leave. Saint Benedict asked Saint Scholastica why she had prayed that way. Saint Scholastica replied that if he would not listen to her requests, then God certainly would, because God is more generous! Take this moment to pray for your sibling to receive God's grace and _____ as a blessing from God!

PLURAL NOUN

FOOD _____

VERB ENDING IN "ING" _____

DAY OF THE WEEK _____

ADJECTIVE _____

YEAR IN SCHOOL _____

ADJECTIVE _____

PLURAL NOUN _____

VERB PAST TENSE _____

ROOM IN HOUSE _____

ANIMAL _____

PLURAL NOUN _____

PLURAL NOUN _____

ANIMAL _____

ADJECTIVE _____

LARGE NUMBER _____

PLURAL FOOD _____

SCHOOL SUBJECT _____

Saved by the Bell

I had just poured a second bowl of my favorite cereal,

_____ -o's, when my mom came _____ into the
FOOD   VERB ENDING IN "ING"

kitchen shouting "Happy _____ !" I asked her what she was
DAY OF THE WEEK

feeling so _____ about, and she reminded me that today was
ADJECTIVE

my first day of _____ . We were going to try a new
YEAR IN SCHOOL

_____ homeschool program. Mom had high hopes and even
ADJECTIVE

asked for the intercession of Saint Elizabeth Ann Seton! She's the

patroness of Catholic schools and _____ , and she inspires my
PLURAL NOUN

mom a lot!

When I _____ into our _____ to start class,
VERB PAST TENSE   ROOM IN HOUSE

things got a little out of hand. First, my baby brother was throwing his

stuffed _____ around the room while screaming,
ANIMAL

" _____ and _____ " over and over again. Just
PLURAL NOUN   PLURAL NOUN

when my mom got him calmed down, our pet _____ walked
ANIMAL

in and started chewing on the _____ school workbook! And
ADJECTIVE

if that wasn't enough, the doorbell rang and when my mom opened the

door, there was a delivery man with _____ _____
LARGE NUMBER   PLURAL FOOD

we didn't even order! My mom took a deep breath and said, "Maybe

we'll take a snack break and try again!"

Did you know . . . ?

Saint Elizabeth Ann Seton (1774–1821) was the first American-born person to be canonized a
saint. She raised her five children after the death of her husband. Then, she founded a religious
community for women, opened the first American parish school, and started the first American
Catholic orphanage. She is an inspiration to parents and teachers who want to prepare their kids to
lead good and holy lives. Next time you're studying for a big test in _____ ,
SCHOOL SUBJECT
ask Saint Elizabeth Ann Seton to pray for you!

PLURAL LARGE OBJECT _____

ADJECTIVE _____

VERB PAST TENSE _____

VERB ENDING IN "ING" _____

NOUN _____

ADJECTIVE _____

FAMILY MEMBER _____

VERB PAST TENSE _____

NUMBER _____

ADVERB _____

ADJECTIVE _____

VERB PAST TENSE _____

LARGE NUMBER _____

FOOD _____

FAVORITE TV SHOW _____

Saint Clare of Assisi

Clare was born in Italy into a family with _____ of

PLURAL LARGE OBJECT

wealth. She lived an affluent and _____ life, until one day she

ADJECTIVE

_____ to see Saint Francis _____ at the local

VERB PAST TENSE   VERB ENDING IN "ING"

church in Assisi. Clare was moved by the words of Saint Francis and she

decided to give all of her _____ to Jesus in a life of

NOUN

_____ poverty.

ADJECTIVE

However, Clare's _____ had chosen a man for her to

FAMILY MEMBER

marry. Clare refused and _____ away to live at San Damiano

VERB PAST TENSE

Church. While living there, God granted her more than _____

NUMBER

miracles. One time, she _____ prayed for God to protect

ADVERB

them from an army. All of a sudden, a/an _____ storm came

ADJECTIVE

and they _____ away! Another time, Clare fed the other

VERB PAST TENSE

_____ sisters at the convent with just one loaf of

LARGE NUMBER

_____ that seemed to multiply as she cut it. Throughout her

FOOD

life, Clare was a great example of being faithful to God.

Did you know . . . ?

Saint Clare (1194–1253) was deeply touched by the words and actions of Saint Francis of Assisi. When she heard Saint Francis preach, she asked him to help her follow Jesus more closely. Saint Clare started the Order of Poor Ladies (now called the Poor Clares) against her parents' wishes. Eventually, her sisters entered the convent, too. When Saint Francis grew ill, Saint Clare took care of him until he died in 1226. Afterward, despite poor health, Saint Clare promoted the growth of her religious order until her own death in 1253. Saint Clare is also the patroness of television, so before you sit down to watch _____ next time, ask her

FAVORITE TV SHOW

to pray for you!

SMALL NUMBER _____

ADVERB _____

ADJECTIVE _____

NOISE _____

NOUN _____

ADVERB _____

ADJECTIVE _____

ADVERB _____

VERB _____

VERB _____

VERB PAST TENSE _____

VERB PAST TENSE _____

PLURAL TYPE OF FLOWER _____

ADJECTIVE _____

NOUN _____

ADJECTIVE _____

FAVORITE PRAYER _____

FOOD _____

TIME OF DAY _____

ADJECTIVE _____

VERB _____

ADVERB _____

Early Morning with Mary

It was _____ in the morning when I was _____
         SMALL NUMBER   ADVERB

woken up from a/an _____ night's sleep by the sound of
                   ADJECTIVE

_____ coming from outside. I looked out my bedroom
     NOISE

_____ and saw that the street was packed with people. They
  NOUN

were _____ singing *Las Mañanitas*, which could only mean
      ADVERB

one thing—it was the feast of Our Lady of Guadalupe!

The crowd waved _____ banners with Our Lady's image
                ADJECTIVE

on them. _____ , people started to _____ and
           ADVERB   VERB

_____ as the crowd processed down the street toward the
  VERB

church entrance.

I _____ up, _____ out the door, and joined
  VERB PAST TENSE   VERB PAST TENSE

everyone in the church. Everyone was laying flowers at the feet of the

statue of Mary. There were so many _____ , the church
                                  PLURAL TYPE OF FLOWER

smelled like a/an _____ _____ . After Mass, we
              ADJECTIVE   NOUN

continued the celebration by watching _____ dancers,
                               ADJECTIVE

praying a _____ , and eating spicy _____ . The
       FAVORITE PRAYER   FOOD

festivities went all the way until _____ and now I'm so
                           TIME OF DAY

_____ all I want to do is _____ !
  ADJECTIVE   VERB

Did you know . . . ?

Every December 12, Catholics around the world—especially those in North America—celebrate the Feast of Our Lady of Guadalupe. On this special day, we honor and thank our Blessed Mother for appearing to Saint Juan Diego on Tepeyac Hill in 1531. We remember Mary's words to us, and we venerate the image she miraculously left on Juan Diego's humble *tilma*, or cloak. Many North American parishes hold all-night vigils before Our Lady's feast day. These churches are packed with faithful parishioners who sing, dance, pray, and celebrate Our Lady of Guadalupe as _____ and proudly as possible!
  ADVERB

NUMBER _____

ADJECTIVE _____

PLURAL NOUN _____

ADJECTIVE _____

ANIMAL _____

BODY PART _____

NOUN _____

NOUN _____

PLURAL BODY PART _____

ADVERB _____

NUMBER _____

PLURAL NOUN _____

NOUN _____

NOUN _____

ADJECTIVE _____

PLURAL BODY PART _____

When I Grow Up

When I grow up I want to be a pediatrician, a doctor who takes care

of patients under _____ years old. For now, I have a/an
NUMBER

_____ doctor's kit that I use to practice doing checkups on
ADJECTIVE

all of my stuffed _____ . Today, I have a full schedule of
PLURAL NOUN

_____ patients.
ADJECTIVE

My first patient is a baby _____ with a sore
ANIMAL

_____ . First, I'll take its temperature with my
BODY PART

_____ . Then, I'll use my _____ to listen to its heart
NOUN   NOUN

and _____ . After that, I'll _____ check its
PLURAL BODY PART   ADVERB

symptoms and tell it to take _____ _____ and call
NUMBER   PLURAL NOUN

me in the morning.

Since they usually behave so well, I let each patient pick a small prize

like a/an _____ or a/an _____ to take home. I love
NOUN   NOUN

taking care of my patients and helping them to feel _____ .
ADJECTIVE

Did you know . . . ?

Saint Gianna Molla (1922–1962) was a pediatrician who became known around the world for risking her life to preserve the life of her unborn baby. When Saint Gianna was pregnant with her fourth child, she developed a dangerous medical condition. But Saint Gianna refused any kind of treatment that might harm her baby. Her heroic decision saved her daughter's life even though it put her own in serious danger. Saint Gianna died one week after the birth of her daughter. Her daughter grew up to be a doctor like her mother. She still travels around the world telling her mother's story. If you became a doctor, would you specialize in helping people with hurting _____ ?
PLURAL BODY PART

VERB ENDING IN "ING" _____

FOOD _____

VERB PAST TENSE _____

ADJECTIVE _____

SCHOOL SUBJECT _____

EXCLAMATION _____

ADJECTIVE _____

TYPE OF CONTAINER _____

ADJECTIVE _____

BODY PART _____

VERB PAST TENSE _____

FOOD _____

PLURAL NOUN _____

ROOM IN HOUSE _____

LARGE NUMBER _____

BODY PART _____

Just Homework?

As soon as we finished _____ my favorite dinner, mac and

VERB ENDING IN "ING"

_____ , I _____ up, excited to show my grandpa the

FOOD   _VERB PAST TENSE_

_____ work I did at school that day! But as I looked through

ADJECTIVE

my backpack, I noticed my _____ worksheet was missing!

SCHOOL SUBJECT

" _____ !" I shouted. "Has anyone seen the _____

EXCLAMATION   _ADJECTIVE_

worksheet that was in my backpack?"

"I think I put it in the recycling _____ . I didn't think you

TYPE OF CONTAINER

needed it anymore," Dad replied.

I was _____ with disappointment! I worked my

ADJECTIVE

_____ off on it! I wanted to make everyone realize how mad I

BODY PART

was, so I yelled, "If I become a saint, that project might have ended up

being a relic someday!" I _____ over to the recycling, dug

VERB PAST TENSE

through the old _____ cartons and shredded

FOOD

_____ , pulled it back out, and hung it on our _____

PLURAL NOUN   _ROOM IN HOUSE_

wall.

Now if I ever get canonized, my project will go on tour and inspire

_____ people in churches around the world!

LARGE NUMBER

Did you know . . . ?

Relics are objects from the lives of the saints. They can be a part of the saint's body (like a bone fragment), a piece of their clothing, or an item they owned. We _venerate_, or show respect, for relics because they help connect us to the holy heroes of our faith. We look to the saints to guide and pray for us as we try to grow in holiness and friendship with God. The saints are our greatest friends—and in heaven, we'll get to hang out with them forever! Who knows? Maybe someone will have a relic of your _____ bone in the future!

BODY PART

ADJECTIVE _____

NUMBER _____

VERB PAST TENSE _____

ADJECTIVE _____

VERB PAST TENSE _____

PLURAL FOOD _____

PLURAL FOOD _____

PLURAL ANIMAL _____

ADJECTIVE _____

LIQUID _____

NOUN _____

NAME OF PERSON IN ROOM _____

NOUN _____

NOUN _____

ADJECTIVE _____

NUMBER _____

NUMBER _____

VERB PAST TENSE _____

EXCLAMATION _____

ROOM IN HOUSE _____

PLACE _____

A Picnic with Friends

It was a/an _____ spring day in Lima, Peru. Martin de
ADJECTIVE

Porres and _____ of his friends _____ out for a/an
NUMBER   VERB PAST TENSE

_____ picnic one day before Mass. Martin shared the faith
ADJECTIVE

with them as they _____ a lovely meal of _____ ,
VERB PAST TENSE   PLURAL FOOD

_____ , and _____ on a log.
PLURAL FOOD   PLURAL ANIMAL

After eating, they played _____ tag and had a/an
ADJECTIVE

_____ balloon fight. Then they laid on the picnic
LIQUID

_____ and looked up at the clouds. _____
NOUN   NAME OF PERSON IN ROOM

saw a/an _____ shaped cloud and Martin saw one that
NOUN

looked like a/an _____ .
NOUN

Just then, they heard the _____ church bells ringing! It
ADJECTIVE

was _____ o'clock, time for Mass, and they were
NUMBER

_____ miles away! No one thought they'd make it, except
NUMBER

Martin who told everyone to hold each other's hands and pray.

Everyone was lifted off the ground and _____ through the
VERB PAST TENSE

air, miraculously landing at church just in time for Mass. All they could

say was " _____ !"
EXCLAMATION

Did you know . . . ?

Saint Martin de Porres (1579–1639) was known as the "Saint of the Broom" because of his humble life of service. As a lay Dominican brother, Saint Martin made it his mission to do everything—even sweep the floor—with great care and love for God and others. Although he didn't really have water balloon fights, God did give him the extraordinary gifts of healing, levitation, the ability to talk to animals, and bilocation, or the capacity to be in two places at once. He could be in the _____ and in the
ROOM IN HOUSE
_____ at the same time!
PLACE

NUMBER _____

VERB PAST TENSE _____

VERB _____

ADJECTIVE _____

VERB PAST TENSE _____

NAME OF RELATIVE _____

NAME OF PERSON IN ROOM _____

VERB PAST TENSE _____

COLOR _____

YOUR BIRTHDATE _____

PLURAL NOUN _____

VERB PAST TENSE _____

FOOD _____

NAME OF PERSON IN ROOM _____

ADJECTIVE _____

ADJECTIVE _____

ADJECTIVE _____

ADJECTIVE _____

NAME OF PERSON IN ROOM _____

SAINT'S NAME _____

It's a Feast Day Somewhere

When I woke up at _____ in the morning and
NUMBER

_____ out of bed to _____ my teeth, it felt like
VERB PAST TENSE   VERB

any other _____ day. But when I _____ into the
ADJECTIVE   VERB PAST TENSE

kitchen, _____ shouted, "Happy Feast of Saint
NAME OF RELATIVE

_____ !" and then _____ bright
NAME OF PERSON IN ROOM   VERB PAST TENSE

_____ confetti in the air! I checked the calendar. It was
COLOR

_____ , the day that this saint laid down their
YOUR BIRTHDATE

_____ for Christ and _____ into Heaven.
PLURAL NOUN   VERB PAST TENSE

To celebrate, we had _____ for breakfast, prayed the
FOOD

litany of _____ , and shared our favorite _____
NAME OF PERSON IN ROOM   ADJECTIVE

stories from the saint's life. We also went to Mass and heard a/an

_____ homily on the _____ virtues we can learn
ADJECTIVE   ADJECTIVE

from them! I was feeling pretty _____ when the day came to
ADJECTIVE

an end, but when I checked the calendar before bed, I saw that

tomorrow is the feast of Saint _____ , so it will be time to
NAME OF PERSON IN ROOM

party all over again!!

Did you know . . . ?

The liturgical calendar is jam-packed with celebrations and feast days in honor of the saints and mysteries of our Catholic faith. From the feast of _____ to the
SAINT'S NAME
Solemnity of the Immaculate Conception, there's always something for Catholic families to celebrate! Whose feast days are coming up this week? Why not choose one of these saints to learn about, and plan a special meal or family activity to celebrate this saint's life?

ADJECTIVE _____	PLURAL NOUN _____
ARTICLE OF CLOTHING _____	LARGE NUMBER _____
TYPE OF CONTAINER _____	VERB _____
LIQUID _____	VERB ENDING IN "ING" _____
PIECE OF FURNITURE _____	VERB _____
ADJECTIVE _____	ADJECTIVE _____
FOOD _____	PLURAL NOUN _____
ANIMAL _____	

Stargazing

When you get an opportunity to go stargazing on a/an

_____ summer night, you must take along a warm
   ADJECTIVE

_____ , a/an _____ filled with delicious hot
ARTICLE OF CLOTHING   TYPE OF CONTAINER

_____ to keep you warm, and a _____ to have
   LIQUID   PIECE OF FURNITURE

something comfortable to sit on. Also, don't forget to pack a/an

_____ snack, such as a peanut butter and _____
   ADJECTIVE   FOOD

sandwich, a yummy pack of _____ crackers, or some gummy
                      ANIMAL

_____ . Maybe your parents have a telescope and a map
   PLURAL NOUN

showing all _____ constellations to help you know what you
          LARGE NUMBER

are seeing. If you are patient and _____ long enough, you
                     VERB

might even see a _____ star. Don't forget to make a wish!
         VERB ENDING IN "ING"

When you _____ to look at the stars, you can't help but think
     VERB

of our amazing God and just how _____ his creation is!
               ADJECTIVE

Did you know . . . ?

When Saint Josephine Bakhita was a little girl in Sudan, way back before she even knew about the Catholic faith, she used to look up at the night sky and ask herself who made all the beautiful lights she could see. She imagined that whoever made the stars in the sky must have been wonderful! After suffering for many years as a slave, Saint Bakhita was finally given her freedom. She went on to become not only a Catholic religious sister but also a canonized saint! When you look up at the night sky, does it remind you of God and all his _____ ?
                            PLURAL NOUN

NAME OF RELATIVE _____

ADJECTIVE _____

COUNTRY _____

ADJECTIVE _____

SMALL NUMBER _____

ADJECTIVE _____

EXCLAMATION _____

LARGE NUMBER _____

PLURAL ANIMAL _____

PLURAL ANIMAL _____

ADJECTIVE _____

VERB PAST TENSE _____

VERB ENDING IN "ING" _____

ADJECTIVE _____

VERB _____

NAME OF PERSON IN ROOM _____

YOUR HOMETOWN _____

Miracle of the Sun

Dear _____ ,
NAME OF RELATIVE

I hope you are having a/an _____ time on your trip to
ADJECTIVE

_____ ! Things back home here in Portugal have been
COUNTRY

_____ ! Three young kids from our village say they have seen
ADJECTIVE

the Blessed Virgin Mary! Only _____ people believed them at
SMALL NUMBER

first, but the other day something _____ happened. The
ADJECTIVE

children told us Mary was going to do something incredible and,

_____ , were they right! We went out into the field with
EXCLAMATION

_____ other people. Even though it was raining
LARGE NUMBER

_____ and _____ , the three children stayed
PLURAL ANIMAL   PLURAL ANIMAL

completely dry! Then, all of a sudden, the _____ sun spun
ADJECTIVE

and _____ in the sky and came _____ down to
VERB PAST TENSE   VERB ENDING IN "ING"

the ground. We were _____ with wonder and awe at the
ADJECTIVE

miracle. Now everyone believes the children are telling the truth. I can't

wait for you to _____ back home!
VERB

  Love,

_____
NAME OF PERSON IN ROOM

Did you know ... ?

In 1917, the Blessed Virgin Mary appeared to three children—siblings Saint Francisco and Saint Jacinta, and their cousin Lucía—in the small town of Fatima, Portugal. Mary shared many messages with the children. She especially encouraged them (and us!) to pray the Rosary, repent of our sins, and live for God. At first, many people doubted what the children told them about Mary and her messages. But on October 13, 1917, the Miracle of the Sun revealed that something supernatural was happening in Fatima. Even atheists in the crowd were convinced! Can you imagine the Blessed Virgin Mary visiting _____ ?
YOUR HOME TOWN

ADJECTIVE _____

VERB PAST TENSE _____

NUMBER _____

ADJECTIVE _____

NUMBER _____

COLOR _____

NOUN _____

NOUN _____

ADJECTIVE _____

ADJECTIVE _____

ADVERB _____

COLOR _____

VERB PAST TENSE _____

ADVERB _____

LARGE NUMBER _____

Help From a Saint

I was feeling _____ as I _____ into the sacristy
               ADJECTIVE   VERB PAST TENSE

to get ready to be an altar server at Mass for the very first time. I tried on

_____ different cassocks, but none of them were right! A few
NUMBER

were too _____ , one was _____ sizes too big, and
         ADJECTIVE   NUMBER

the rest were _____ ! I decided to wait for the older server to
              COLOR

arrive.

    As I waited, I tried to remember all of my jobs that I had during Mass.

I couldn't remember if I had to hold the _____ first or bring
                                 NOUN

the _____ to the priest. I started to get nervous. What if I did
      NOUN

a/an _____ job!?
        ADJECTIVE

    Just then, the Sacristy door opened. "Hi! My name is Lorenzo Ruiz.

You must be the _____ server I will be serving with today," he
              ADJECTIVE

said with a smile. He _____ helped me pick out the right
             ADVERB

cassock (the rope needed to be _____ that day) and told me
                     COLOR

I had nothing to worry about as long as I _____ at the right
                         VERB PAST TENSE

time. My nervousness went away and I was able to _____
                                   ADVERB

serve the Mass.

Did you know . . . ?

Saint Lorenzo Ruiz was born in the Philippines around 1600. As a boy, he served his parish as an altar server and now is the patron saint of altar servers. He also was a gifted calligrapher, copying church documents in beautiful penmanship. When he grew up, he married and had two sons and a daughter. He sailed to Japan, a country where Christianity was illegal. He was arrested and the government officials tried to get him to give up his faith. Instead, he told them that if he had _____ lives to give, he would offer them all to God.
                      LARGE NUMBER

ADJECTIVE _____

FAMOUS PERSON _____

NAME OF PERSON IN ROOM _____

FAMOUS PERSON _____

LAST NAME _____

NOUN _____

ADJECTIVE _____

ANIMAL _____

NAME OF PERSON IN ROOM _____

ADJECTIVE _____

ARTICLE OF CLOTHING _____

FAMOUS PERSON _____

FAMOUS PERSON _____

FOOD _____

ARTICLE OF CLOTHING _____

ADJECTIVE _____

LETTER OF THE ALPHABET _____

SOMETHING YOU LIKE _____

Famous Folks

My second-grade class has been learning about famous people who

have done _____ things in history. It has been so interesting
ADJECTIVE

learning about the great _____ , President
FAMOUS PERSON

_____ , and the literary work of _____ .
NAME OF PERSON IN ROOM   FAMOUS PERSON

Our teacher, Mr. _____ , assigned each
LAST NAME

_____ in our class a different historical figure to research and
NOUN

write a report on. I was assigned Saint Kateri, the first Native American

saint! She lived such an inspiring and _____ life.
ADJECTIVE

Next week, we get to dress up as our famous person and give a short

speech on why they are famous. As Saint Kateri, I will be wearing a/an

_____ skin dress and carrying a lily because she was known
ANIMAL

as the Lily of the Mohawks. It will be so fun seeing _____
NAME OF PERSON IN ROOM

with a/an _____ _____ on like _____
ADJECTIVE   ARTICLE OF CLOTHING   FAMOUS PERSON

would wear. My best friend will be dressing as _____ ,
FAMOUS PERSON

inventor of the _____ sandwich. Even our teacher is dressing
FOOD

up as Abraham Lincoln with a top _____ and a/an
ARTICLE OF CLOTHING

_____ beard. I sure hope I get a/an _____ +
ADJECTIVE   LETTER OF THE ALPHABET

on my report.

Did you know . . . ?

Saint Kateri Tekakwitha (1656–1680) was a Native American who converted to Catholicism at the age of nineteen. She decided to do this even though many of her family and friends were against it. Saint Kateri had to leave her village in upstate New York and join a community of Native American converts to Christianity in Canada. She spent five years with this community and the Jesuits who founded it. When Saint Kateri died at the young age of twenty-three, the scars on her face (from a case of childhood smallpox) miraculously vanished! Would you be willing to give up _____ to follow Jesus?
SOMETHING YOU LIKE

ADJECTIVE _____

DAY OF THE WEEK _____

ADJECTIVE _____

ADJECTIVE ENDING IN "EST" _____

PLURAL FOOD _____

LIQUID _____

LARGE NUMBER _____

PLURAL NOUN _____

PLURAL NOUN _____

NAME OF PERSON IN ROOM _____

NUMBER _____

NOUN _____

BODY PART _____

NAME OF PERSON IN ROOM _____

FAMOUS PERSON _____

VERB ENDING IN "ING" _____

NAME OF RELATIVE _____

The Half-Bearded Man

The funniest thing happened at a fancy and _____ party I
ADJECTIVE

attended last _____ ! It was a/an _____ event,
DAY OF THE WEEK   ADJECTIVE

where only the richest and _____ were invited. Each
ADJECTIVE ENDING IN "EST"

plate of _____ and glass of _____ at the party
PLURAL FOOD   LIQUID

cost at least _____ dollars and the decorations included
LARGE NUMBER

fancy _____ and expensive _____ .
PLURAL NOUN   PLURAL NOUN

Everyone was eager for a special guest, Philip Neri, to arrive. Philip is

a very holy man, and everyone was impressed he accepted

_____ 's invitation. About _____ hours into
NAME OF PERSON IN ROOM   NUMBER

the party, we heard a/an _____ at the door. When the host
NOUN

opened the door, in walked the strangest man I've ever seen! It was

Philip, and he had only half a beard on his _____ . We all
BODY PART

gasped! I haven't been this shocked since _____ showed
NAME OF PERSON IN ROOM

up with _____ to my last party.
FAMOUS PERSON

At first, everyone was quiet until Philip started _____ .
VERB ENDING IN "ING"

Then we all started laughing and we realized how silly it was.

Did you know . . . ?

Saint Philip Neri (1515–1595) was an Italian priest known for his sense of humor, his care for
the poor and marginalized, and his bold witness to Christ. The story of Saint Philip shaving half
his beard is just one example of how he lived all three! Saint Philip shaved his beard because
he wanted to teach the party host an important lesson. He knew the rich host had invited him
to his party for selfish reasons. The host wanted to be seen with Saint Philip so that people
would think he was as good and holy as Saint Philip was. Saint Philip made a fool of himself to
help this man see how prideful he was being, so that he might repent. Have you ever played a
practical joke on _____ ?
NAME OF RELATIVE

PLURAL LETTER IN THE ALPHABET _____

SCHOOL SUBJECT _____

ADJECTIVE ENDING IN "EST" _____

TITLE OF LEADER _____

SPORT _____

BODY PART _____

PLURAL NOUN _____

FAVORITE GAME _____

FAVORITE PRAYER _____

ANIMAL _____

VERB _____

PLURAL BODY PART _____

ADJECTIVE _____

FAVORITE CHRISTMAS CAROL

_____

The Clumsy Saint

My older brother has it all together. He gets straight

_____ on all of his _____ tests, he's the
PLURAL LETTER OF THE ALPHABET   SCHOOL SUBJECT

_____ kid in school, and he's the _____ of
ADJECTIVE ENDING IN "EST"   TITLE OF LEADER

the _____ team.
SPORT

    I, on the other _____ , struggle to do well in school,
BODY PART

especially when it comes to tests about _____ , I'm too
PLURAL NOUN

clumsy to make the _____ team, and I even forgot the
FAVORITE GAME

_____ during a faith formation class!
FAVORITE PRAYER

    Seeing how great my brother is makes me as jealous as a/an

_____ . When I told my mom how I felt, she told me about a
ANIMAL

boy who lived a long time ago named Joseph who wasn't perfect either.

He would _____ around and get lost, he was so clumsy that
VERB

he tripped over his own _____ , and he struggled in school.
PLURAL BODY PART

But, he persevered and became a priest and eventually a saint!

    She reminded me that God gives us different talents and only by his

grace will we become more _____ . Now I know you don't
ADJECTIVE

have to be perfect to be on the path to holiness!

Did you know . . . ?

Saint Joseph of Cupertino (1603–1663) enjoyed a deep relationship with God. In fact, Saint Joseph's love for God was so strong, he often went into ecstasy and levitated. Just the thought of God could make him fly off the ground with joy! One famous incident happened during Christmas Eve Mass. When the musicians began to play a carol, Saint Joseph suddenly floated high above the altar in front of everyone. Do you think the carol that lifted him off the ground with joy was

_____ ?
FAVORITE CHRISTMAS CAROL

ADJECTIVE _____

VERB ENDING IN "S" _____

TYPE OF WEATHER _____

FAMOUS PERSON _____

ADJECTIVE _____

ADJECTIVE _____

COLOR _____

ADJECTIVE _____

PLURAL TYPE OF PLANT _____

ANIMAL _____

VERB PAST TENSE _____

ADVERB _____

ADJECTIVE _____

VERB PAST TENSE _____

ADJECTIVE _____

PLURAL TYPE OF FLOWER _____

May Crowning

Today is the _____ day when our whole parish

ADJECTIVE

_____ together for the May Crowning, where we place a

VERB ENDING IN "S"

crown of flowers on the statue of Mary! The morning was

_____ and we met outside the church to get started. My

TYPE OF WEATHER

friend _____ was helping out as the _____ altar

FAMOUS PERSON   ADJECTIVE

server! This year my brother and I got to help too! We made the crown

with _____ flowers like _____ roses,

ADJECTIVE   COLOR

_____ tulips, and fragrant _____ .

ADJECTIVE   PLURAL TYPE OF PLANT

Unfortunately, things didn't go as planned. As soon as we started, a

big _____ ran by and _____ at the crown of

ANIMAL   VERB PAST TENSE

flowers. My brother chased after it as _____ as he could, but

ADVERB

it was no use—the _____ crown was ruined! Thankfully, we

ADJECTIVE

all _____ and worked together to make a new crown from

VERB PAST TENSE

the flowers planted around the base of the statue and it turned out

absolutely _____ ! Happy May, Mary!!

ADJECTIVE

Did you know . . . ?

Because Jesus ascended into heaven as the King of kings and of the Universe, when Mary died and was assumed into Heaven, she became the Queen of Heaven and Earth. The May Crowning is a traditional Catholic ritual in which we honor the Blessed Virgin Mary as Queen of the month of May—and more importantly, as Queen of Heaven! You can participate by organizing friends to do a May Crowning at your church, or you can even do one at home with a statue of the Blessed Virgin that your family has! Don't forget to include _____ in Mary's crown!

PLURAL TYPE OF FLOWER

PLURAL ANIMAL _____

ADJECTIVE _____

ADJECTIVE _____

PLURAL NOUN _____

FAMOUS PERSON _____

NAME OF PERSON IN ROOM _____

EXCLAMATION _____

NUMBER _____

ADJECTIVE _____

NAME OF MALE IN ROOM _____

FOOD _____

PLURAL NOUN _____

NUMBER _____

ADJECTIVE _____

CITY _____

ROOM IN HOUSE _____

LARGE NUMBER _____

TYPE OF CANDY _____

NUMBER _____

FAVORITE GAME _____

The All Saints Day Quiz Show

HOST: Welcome friends and _____ to the first ever All Saints

PLURAL ANIMAL
Day Quiz Show! We've got two _____ contestants here ready

ADJECTIVE
to answer _____ questions about everyone's favorite saints!

ADJECTIVE
Time for our first question: who is the patron saint of _____ ?

PLURAL NOUN

CONTESTANT 1: Saint _____ ?

FAMOUS PERSON

HOST: Ooooh, so close, but that's incorrect.

CONTESTANT 2: Saint _____ ?

NAME OF PERSON IN ROOM

HOST: _____ ! You got it! _____ points!! Okay,

EXCLAMATION   NUMBER
the next question is even more _____ than the first: Saint

ADJECTIVE
_____ is the patron saint of what?

NAME OF MALE IN ROOM

CONTESTANT 1: I know! He's the patron of _____ and

FOOD
_____ !

PLURAL NOUN

HOST: You got it! _____ points to you! Alright, time for the

NUMBER
final question. Where was the most recent and most _____

ADJECTIVE
apparition of the Blessed Virgin Mary?

CONTESTANT 2: _____ !

CITY OR TOWN

HOST: Oh, I'm sorry, no.

CONTESTANT 1: In our _____ ?

ROOM IN HOUSE

HOST: Ding Ding! Congratulations!! You are the winner of our grand
prize: _____ rosaries made out of _____ ! You

LARGE NUMBER   TYPE OF CANDY
can pray and eat at the same time! Thanks for playing! We'll see you in
_____ years for our next All Saints Day Quiz Show!

NUMBER

Did you know . . . ?

The Solemnity of All Saints, celebrated every year on November 1, is a great reminder of the great and holy heroes who have gone before us. The saints in Heaven are not simply far away now that they're not alive. They are always present, through the power of God, in our lives and most especially at every Mass we attend. They're cheering you on every time you go to confession because they want you to get back up and to keep running the race. They're even with you when you are playing _____ .

FAVORITE GAME

NOUN _____

ADJECTIVE _____

ADJECTIVE _____

PLURAL ANIMAL _____

NOUN _____

PLURAL OCCUPATION _____

PLURAL NOUN _____

EXCLAMATION _____

NAME OF PERSON IN ROOM _____

PLURAL NOUN _____

VERB _____

SEA CREATURE _____

VERB _____

NAME OF PERSON IN ROOM _____

ADJECTIVE _____

PRAYER _____

NOUN _____

VERB _____

PLURAL NOUN _____

Ahoy Matey

Yo ho ho! My best friends and I are playing explorers in our play

_____ . Our ship has set sail on the _____ sea to
        NOUN   ADJECTIVE

find _____ treasure! With my best explorer voice, I yell, "All ye
       ADJECTIVE

sea _____ swab the _____ and keep watch for
    PLURAL ANIMAL   NOUN

_____ trying to steal our _____ and booty!"
PLURAL OCCUPATION   PLURAL NOUN

" _____ , Captain!" my friends shout back.
    EXCLAMATION

_____ is the best lookout. S/he takes a look through
NAME OF PERSON IN ROOM

the spyglass and yells, "Shiver me _____ ! Trouble ahead! A
                                      PLURAL NOUN

pirate ship is a-comin'!"

If they attack and take over our ship, they'll make us _____
                                                              VERB

the plank for sure and we'll be _____ bait! But, how
                                    SEA CREATURE

should we defend our ship? My first mate thinks we should

_____ and most of us agree. But _____
       VERB   NAME OF PERSON IN ROOM

reminded us of Saint Rose of Lima who once defeated pirates by just by

praying. As captain, I make a/an _____ decision to imitate
                                     ADJECTIVE

Saint Rose and we all say a/an _____ . Then I say, "Heave ho
                                    PRAYER

all you explorers! The pirate's _____ is turning around!"
                                    NOUN

We all _____ with excitement. Our ship is safe for today.
          VERB

Did you know . . . ?

Saint Rose of Lima (1586–1617) was a third order Dominican from Lima, Peru. The story of Saint Rose and the pirates shows us the power of her prayer! When pirates invaded Lima in 1615, many people ran into the church to hide, including Saint Rose. She convinced everyone that they should pray instead of fighting back. She was confident that God would protect them. When the pirates came into the church, they saw Saint Rose aflame with light and holding a monstrance with the Blessed Sacrament. The sight scared the pirates away! Have you ever prayed to protect yourself from dangerous _____ ?
                                                                                PLURAL NOUN

LENGTH OF TIME _____

VERB _____

NAME OF RELATIVE _____

ADJECTIVE _____

ANIMAL _____

ADJECTIVE _____

NAME OF MALE IN THE ROOM _____

ANIMAL _____

LARGE NUMBER _____

PLURAL ANIMAL _____

VERB PAST TENSE _____

ADJECTIVE _____

ANIMAL _____

PLURAL PLANT _____

EXCLAMATION _____

ADJECTIVE _____

PLURAL BODY PART _____

ANIMAL NOISE _____

NAME OF FAMILY PET _____

ADJECTIVE _____

ANIMAL _____

Animals at Mass

Once every _____ , the whole family gets to

LENGTH OF TIME

_____ to Mass together. And by "whole family" I mean

VERB

_____ , my siblings, my _____ cousins, and even our

NAME OF RELATIVE · ADJECTIVE

beloved pet _____ ! Yep, that's right! It's the _____

ANIMAL · ADJECTIVE

feast of Saint Francis!

Father _____ starts the Mass outside with the blessing of

NAME OF MALE IN ROOM

the animals. This year there was a/an _____ on a leash,

ANIMAL

_____ _____ who _____ over each

LARGE NUMBER · PLURAL ANIMAL · VERB PAST TENSE

other, and even a/an _____ _____ who ate some of

ADJECTIVE · ANIMAL

the _____ in the courtyard of the church! _____ ,

PLURAL TYPE OF PLANT · EXCLAMATION

it sure can be loud and _____ with all those animals around!

ADJECTIVE

When Father extended his _____ over the group of animals

PLURAL BODY PART

and said the blessing, our pet let out a loud " _____ ." I'm

ANIMAL NOISE

not sure if _____ is any holier after the blessing, but Father

NAME OF FAMILY PET

said hopefully it will help him be less _____ !

ADJECTIVE

Did you know . . . ?

Saint Francis of Assisi (c. 1182–1226) is the patron saint of animals because he had a deep love for God's creation. Saint Francis saw and marveled at the creativity of God reflected in every plant, animal, and person. He even preached to the animals, who would stop what they were doing to listen to Saint Francis! In honor of this special saint, many parishes offer a blessing for pets on October 4, the Feast of Saint Francis. Most people bring typical family pets like dogs, cats, or hamsters. Some people at your parish, though, might bring a chicken, an iguana, or maybe even a/an _____ !

ANIMAL

NAME OF RELATIVE _____

ADJECTIVE _____

ADJECTIVE _____

VERB ENDING IN "ING" _____

NOUN _____

ADJECTIVE _____

ANIMAL _____

ANIMAL NOISE ENDING IN "ING"

_____

PLURAL NOUN _____

PLURAL BODY PART _____

VERB PAST TENSE _____

NOUN _____

ANIMAL _____

VERB ENDING IN "ING" _____

ADJECTIVE _____

ADVERB _____

ADJECTIVE _____

Things That Go Bump

Every night before bed, _____ and I read a book together. I
NAME OF RELATIVE

usually love it, but tonight we picked out a/an _____ and
ADJECTIVE

scary book, and I had a/an _____ time falling asleep.
ADJECTIVE

First, I thought I heard something _____ on my window. I
VERB ENDING IN "ING"

called for my mom, and she said it was just a/an _____
NOUN

outside. That made me feel a little _____ , but then I heard a
ADJECTIVE

big _____ _____ outside. There were shadows
ANIMAL   ANIMAL NOISE ENDING IN "ING"

on the walls in my room that looked like scary _____ . Even
PLURAL NOUN

when I shut my _____ tight, I could still imagine them.
PLURAL BODY PART

I called for my mom again. This time, she _____ on the light
VERB PAST TENSE

and showed me there really wasn't anything scary in my room. We looked

out my bedroom _____ together and saw my pet
NOUN

_____ _____ on the fence. It was just her all along!
ANIMAL   VERB ENDING IN "ING"

Then my mom read me a/an _____ story to help me relax
ADJECTIVE

and we said a quick prayer together. This time when she turned off the

light and left the room, I _____ fell asleep.
ADVERB

Did you know . . . ?

Saint Teresa of Avila (1515–1582) was a Spanish Carmelite nun and mystic. She had a deep prayer life, and her books and writings have helped countless Christians grow closer to God through prayer. Saint Teresa also left us a great prayer for when we are scared or anxious: "Let nothing disturb you. Let nothing frighten you. All things pass away: God never changes. Patience obtains all things. One who has God lacks nothing. God alone suffices." Try saying this prayer when you feel _____ .
ADJECTIVE

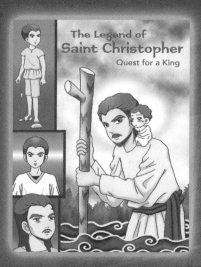

The Legend of
Saint Christopher
Quest for a King

Saint Clare of Assisi
Runaway Rich Girl

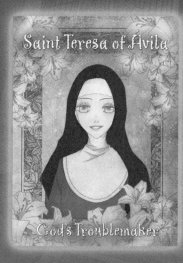

Saint Teresa of Ávila

God's Troublemaker

Philip Neri

The
Laughing
Saint

Gospel TimeTrekkers

Three ordinary kids, six extraordinary adventures, one incredible quest!

The Gospel Time Trekkers, a six-book series, follows the adventures of three siblings as they travel back to Gospel times to find Jesus and discover him in their everyday lives. Remaining true to biblical culture and scholarship, these historical fiction books offer a creative presentation of Christian faith and values. Through imaginative retellings of important scriptural events, children personally encounter Jesus and experience what it was like to live in his time.

Gospel Time Trekkers #1
Shepherds to the Rescue

Written by
Maria Grace Dateno, FSP

Illustrated by
Paul Cunningham

Gospel Time Trekkers #2
Braving the Storm

Written by
Maria Grace Dateno, FSP

Illustrated by
Paul Cunningham

Gospel Time Trekkers #3
Danger at Sea

Written by
Maria Grace Dateno, FSP

Illustrated by
Paul Cunningham

Gospel Time Trekkers #4
Mystery of the Missing Jars

Written by
Maria Grace Dateno, FSP

Illustrated by
Paul Cunningham

Gospel Time Trekkers #5
Courageous Quest

Written by
Maria Grace Dateno, FSP

Illustrated by
Paul Cunningham

Gospel Time Trekkers #6
Discovery at Dawn

Written by
Maria Grace Dateno, FSP

Illustrated by
Paul Cunningham

If you like
Catholic Funny Fill-Ins,
you'll love the rest of the
Fill-Ins series
by Karen and Tommy Tighe!

All three books in
the Fill-Ins series feature more
goofy phrases, more word
puzzles, and more family fun.

Keep an eye out for
Pauline Books & Media's
next book in the Fill-Ins series,
coming soon!

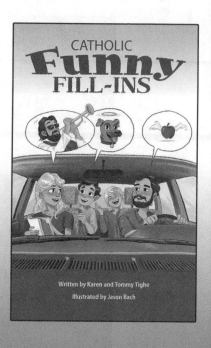

Jason Bach

A proud native of Portland, Oregon, Jason grew up reading *Calvin and Hobbes* and dreaming of being a professional cartoonist. He currently lives in the Washington, D.C., area and, when he is not drawing up new entries in his ongoing series of Catholic comics (www.jasonbachcartoons.com), he works as a graphic designer and illustrator for Coronation Media. In addition to illustrating the *Catholic Funny Fill-Ins* series, he has also contributed illustrations to *The Church Rocks* for Pauline Books & Media.

Who are the Daughters of St. Paul?

We are Catholic sisters with a mission. Our task is to bring the love of Jesus to everyone like Saint Paul did. You can find us in over 50 countries. Our founder, Blessed James Alberione, showed us how to reach out to the world through the media. That's why we publish books, make movies and apps, record music, broadcast on radio, perform concerts, help people at our bookstores, visit parishes, host JClub book fairs, use social media and the Internet, and pray for all of you.

Visit our web site at www.pauline.org

** BOOKS & MEDIA**

The Daughters of St. Paul operate book and media centers at the following addresses. Visit, call, or write the one nearest you today, or find us at www.paulinestore.org.

CALIFORNIA
3908 Sepulveda Blvd, Culver City, CA 90230 — 310-397-8676
3250 Middlefield Road, Menlo Park, CA 94025 — 650-562-7060

FLORIDA
145 SW 107th Avenue, Miami, FL 33174 — 305-559-6715

HAWAII
1143 Bishop Street, Honolulu, HI 96813 — 808-521-2731

ILLINOIS
172 North Michigan Avenue, Chicago, IL 60601 — 312-346-4228

LOUISIANA
4403 Veterans Memorial Blvd, Metairie, LA 70006 — 504-887-7631

MASSACHUSETTS
885 Providence Hwy, Dedham, MA 02026 — 781-326-5385

MISSOURI
9804 Watson Road, St. Louis, MO 63126 — 314-965-3512

NEW YORK
115 E. 29th Street, New York City, NY 10016 — 212-754-1110

SOUTH CAROLINA
243 King Street, Charleston, SC 29401 — 843-577-0175

TEXAS
No book center; for parish exhibits or outreach evangelization, contact:
210-569-0500 or SanAntonio@paulinemedia.com
or P.O. Box 761416, San Antonio, TX 78245

VIRGINIA
1025 King Street, Alexandria, VA 22314 — 703-549-3806

CANADA
3022 Dufferin Street, Toronto, ON M6B 3T5 — 416-781-9131

smile
God loves you